Reading Essentials
in Social Studies

TEACHING AND ASSESSMENT RESOURCE

U.S. Government

PERFECTION LEARNING®

Editorial Director: Susan C. Thies
Editor: Lucy Miller
Writer: Barb Farup

Design Director: Randy Messer
Cover Design: Michael A. Aspengren
Book Design: Deborah Lea Bell, Dea Marks

Image Credits: ClipArt.com(some images copyright www.arttoday.com): pp. 6, 7, 8, 9, 10, 35, 46, 49, 57, 59, 60, 72; Corel: p. 5; Photos.com: pp. 28, 45, 49; Photos.com, NARA, Library of Congress: pp. 16, 31; NARA: p. 36; Supreme Court Curator: pp. 22, 81; PLC: pp. 17, 42, 68

For information, contact
Perfection Learning® Corporation
1000 North Second Avenue, P.O. Box 500
Logan, Iowa 51546-0500.
Phone: 1-800-831-4190 • Fax: 1-800-543-2745
perfectionlearning.com
Printed in the United States of America

2 3 4 5 6 PP 13 12 11 10 09 08
ISBN-10: 0-7891-6228-8 ISBN-13: 978-0-7891-6228-1

Table of Contents

Reading Essentials in Social Studies

Elections and Political Parties

The Executive Branch

continued

Table of Contents *continued*

Reading Essentials
in Social Studies

> " 'Begin at the beginning,' the king said gravely,
> 'and go till you come to the end; then stop.' "
> Lewis Carroll,
> *Alice's Adventures in Wonderland*, (1865), p. 12

Unfortunately, this is the way many learners read—from beginning to end—regardless of the reading task in front of them, whether it be reading for information or pleasure, expository or narrative. This passive, linear approach to text compromises understanding and reading success. Successful readers need to be actively involved in the reading process, monitoring their understanding, personally relating to the text, and applying what they know to understand what they're reading.

While active reading strategies are important to the comprehension of any type of reading material, they are especially important in understanding informational, or expository, text. It is estimated that about 90 percent of adult reading is to acquire information, while only about 10 percent is for pleasure. So content literacy skills will be important to students far beyond their school years. In their interactions with informational text, student readers should be learning content while developing the literacy and thinking skills necessary to become lifelong readers.

Reading Essentials in Social Studies helps readers learn more about concepts introduced in social studies and develop content literacy strategies. Few students ever develop a passion for reading from their social studies textbooks. The interesting, visually appealing, reader-friendly student books in *Reading Essentials in Social Studies* provide essential content and content-area reading practice as they pique students' interest. And the content literacy skills and strategies presented and practiced in the accompanying activities in the strand resources will prepare students for a lifetime of enjoyable and meaningful literacy experiences.

Overview of the Program

Reading Essentials in Social Studies offers curricular-aligned informational books for students in grades 3 to 6, strand resources for practice and assessment of content and content literacy strategies, and a program resource for teaching content literacy strategies.

Reading Essentials in Social Studies Student Books

The interesting and informative nonfiction titles are 40 to 48 pages in length and arranged in thematic strands with five related books per strand. The social studies strands are organized using the following disciplines: American History, Government, Geography, and World History.

Reading Essentials in Social Studies Teaching and Assessment Resources

The reproducible strand resources offer students opportunities to extend content knowledge and develop and practice content literacy strategies. Additionally, twenty-question objective tests and performance-based assessment suggestions are provided for each title to monitor student growth. These comprehensive resources have a separate section for each of the five titles in the strands.

Reading Essentials Content-Area Literacy Strategies Resource

This collection of research-based content literacy strategies will help you make the best use of the student books and the practice and assessment activities in the strand resource.

Rationale: Why Teach Content-Area Reading?

Many mistakenly believe that students do not need further reading instruction once they learn to decode. However, reading goes beyond mere decoding. Content comprehension is dependent upon an active relationship between the reader and the text. Teaching reading in the content areas helps learners make connections between what they know and the new information in the text.

In order to develop content-area knowledge, students need interesting, relevant content-area books. Additionally, students need to develop and practice content-area strategies to learn to interact with the text and create meaning. Many readers have never been taught that they need to think when they are reading and to create pictures in their minds. Reading is not passive word calling. Readers who are not actively involved in their reading, who aren't monitoring their understanding by personally relating to the text and applying what they know to understand what they're reading, will finish with little or no understanding of what they've read. Often they lose confidence in themselves as readers, give up on reading, and fall behind.

The social studies titles and content-area literacy skills and strategies presented and practiced in the *Reading Essentials in Social Studies* program will help students learn how to learn, enabling them to acquire knowledge independently from their reading in school and throughout their lives.

U.S. Government

U.S. Government Student Books

The five titles in the U.S. Government series are *Elections and Political Parties*, *The Executive Branch*, *The Judicial Branch*, *The Legislative Branch*, and *State and Local Government*. Each title offers information about that aspect of U.S. government, including a history of the topic and issues and events that have shaped the way the system works today. Each title features an index and a glossary. The content-specific vocabulary included in the glossary is bolded throughout the text. Additionally, Internet sites are provided to extend the information presented within each chapter.

The *Reading Essentials in Social Studies* U.S. Government titles contain considerate text that is well organized and clearly written. In this way, readers are actively involved in their learning as they make connections and create meaning.

U.S. Government Teaching and Assessment Resource

This comprehensive resource covers all five titles in the strand. Each title-specific section offers

- a synopsis of the chapters in the student book

- reading exploration activities (prereading, during reading, and postreading)

    In order for students to understand the new information presented in the books, they need to relate what they're reading to what they already know. The prereading activities help learners call up prior knowledge and make connections to what they're learning. The during-reading and postreading suggestions provide students with a purpose for reading and guide them in using active reading strategies.

- a content-specific vocabulary activity

    Research shows that vocabulary knowledge is one of the most important factors in increased comprehension.

- two reading skills activities

    Reading skills activities link essential reading skills and strategies with important content.

- a writing activity

    As students write, they make personal connections between the content and themselves.

- a content-area activity

    As students complete activities related to the content, they extend their subject matter knowledge.

- ten project suggestions

    The performance-based activities offer students alternative ways to extend their learning and/or demonstrate their understanding.

- a twenty-question objective test

    Objective assessment is presented in a format similar to the questions on state and standardized tests.

Second Language Learners

The terms English for Speakers of Other Languages (ESOL), English as a Second Language (ESL), or English Language Learners (ELL) were developed to recognize students whose heritage language is other than English. Classrooms today are comprised of a rich variety of heritages and languages reflecting the diverse cultural nature of our society. The Limited English Proficiency (LEP) students enter the classroom at various limited English language levels. They are faced with challenging content in an unfamiliar language. An appropriate instructional model must be in place for these students. ESOL instruction is designed to meet the needs of LEP students by providing instruction based on their level of English proficiency.

When developing and enriching instruction through ESOL strategies, the educator must be sensitive to the student's first language and cultural background while at the same time encouraging the student to acquire the English language in a nonthreatening and productive learning environment. The student's individual differences and learning styles must also be considered when applying ESOL strategies. All LEP students are entitled to equal educational opportunities that include access to materials, programs, and experiences.

Using Reading Essentials in Social Studies with Limited English Students

The *Reading Essentials in Social Studies* program offers LEP students an opportunity to learn grade-level content as they acquire proficiency in the English language. Through the use of certain instructional strategies, LEP students, representing a diverse group of language backgrounds and individual differences, can find success with the same books that are being enjoyed by their English-speaking classmates.

The use of graphic organizers is an effective ESOL strategy. Flow charts, pie charts, family trees, Venn diagrams, etc., are all appropriate and recommended. Additionally, cooperative learning groups offer support and nonthreatening learning environments for LEP students as they develop linguistic and academic skills.

The additional strategies shown below should be used at certain times throughout the lesson to help each student's individual language development and to help him or her progress to a proficient English language level.

Before Reading

Content-area vocabulary is provided on the inside front covers of all *Reading Essentials in Social Studies* titles. While all students benefit from the preteaching of content vocabulary, it is critical for LEP students. They cannot rely on context clues and general background knowledge to the extent their English-language peers can. Introduce the vocabulary in context and use picture cues with vocabulary definitions to ensure understanding.

Below are some specific strategies that will better prepare LEP students to access the core content information in *Reading Essentials in Social Studies*.

- Encourage communication in the classroom setting. LEP students learn so much by listening to their peers.

- Develop predictions based on cover art and book titles. Many of the *Reading Essentials in Social Studies* books include images that are recognizable to English-speaking students but won't be to LEP students. Make sure images and their relationship to the content are clearly explained.

- Use graphic organizers. Build webs around content vocabulary introduced to expand language acquisition and deepen understanding.

- Make the language comprehensible through the use of gestures, visuals, concrete examples, and oral communication.

- Use the suggested activities in this teacher resource to build background knowledge. Restate, expand, paraphrase, repeat, and speak clearly and slowly.

During Reading

The Reading Essentials in Social Studies books are filled with colorful, descriptive visuals. Use the graphics to create meaning for your students. Study and discuss the visuals as well as the text.

Additionally, the following specific strategies will help LEP students acquire the core knowledge presented in the *Reading Essentials in Social Studies* books.

- Continuously refer to the vocabulary in context.

- Draw on students' personal experiences to add meaning to the discussion.

- Provide for much discussion and encourage students to contribute through their thoughts, questions, and opinions.

- Allow oral and written responses to accommodate individual differences.

- Provide time for directed dialogue between student pairs and between teacher and student.

- Encourage journal writing: reflective, descriptive, and expository.

- Tape selections for students.

- Allow for an extended response time. LEP students need time to process their thoughts and responses in an unfamiliar language.

After Reading

In addition to the reading, writing, and content-area activities provided in this resource, use the following strategies with your LEP students to extend and assess the content information presented.

- Encourage students to express personal reactions through written, oral, or pictorial activities.

- Arrange students in cooperative groups to complete the reading, writing, and content-area activities.

- Provide students an opportunity to demonstrate their understanding through one of the project ideas.

- Offer students a chance to complete the twenty-question objective test orally rather than in writing.

Skills and Strategies Chart
U.S. Government

The following chart shows the essential reading, writing, vocabulary, speaking, listening, and viewing skills presented and practiced in the activities in *U.S. Government Teaching and Assessment Resource*.

Reading Essentials	Elections and Political Parties	The Executive Branch	The Judicial Branch	The Legislative Branch	State and Local Government
Analyzing Information				✔	
Comparing and Contrasting				✔	
Determining Cause and Effect			✔		
Distinguishing Fact and Opinion	✔				
Evaluating			✔		✔
Identifying Time Order		✔			
Reading and Using Charts, Graphs, and Diagrams	✔			✔	
Recalling Facts	✔				
Recognizing Main Idea and Details		✔	✔		
Sequencing		✔			
Understanding Multiple Meanings				✔	
Using Prereading Strategies	✔	✔	✔	✔	✔
Writing Essentials					
Researching		✔	✔	✔	
Using the Writing Process			✔		✔
Writing a Biography		✔			
Writing an Editorial				✔	
Writing a Letter	✔				
Writing to Describe				✔	
Writing to Inform			✔		
Writing to Persuade	✔			✔	
Writing to Summarize				✔	✔
Vocabulary Essentials					
Alphabetizing	✔		✔		
Building Content-Area Vocabulary	✔	✔	✔	✔	✔
Classifying					✔
Using a Glossary/Dictionary	✔		✔	✔	
Speaking, Listening, and Viewing Essentials					
Speaking to Inform		✔	✔	✔	
Speaking to Persuade	✔		✔	✔	
Visual Literacy	✔	✔	✔	✔	✔

National Social Studies Standards Correlation

The following chart lists the ten themes as determined by the National Council of Social Studies that form the framework for the teaching of social studies at grades K–12. The content within the five books in the U.S. Government strand in *Reading Essentials in Social Studies* supports the national standards as shown below.

I. Culture	Compare similarities and differences in the ways groups, societies, and cultures meet human needs and concerns.
	Explain and give examples of how language, literature, the arts, architecture, other artifacts, traditions, beliefs, values, and behaviors contribute to the development and transmission of culture.
II. Time, Continuity, and Change	Identify and use key concepts such as chronology, causality, change, conflict, and complexity to explain, analyze, and show connections among patterns of historical change and continuity.
	Identify and describe selected historical periods and patterns of change within and across cultures, such as the rise of civilizations, the development of transportation systems, the growth and breakdown of colonial systems, and others.
III. People, Places, and Environments	
IV. Individual Development and Identity	Identify and describe ways regional, ethnic, and national cultures influence individuals' daily lives.
	Identify and describe the influence of perception, attitudes, values, and beliefs on personal identity.

continued

V. Individuals, Groups, and Institutions	Demonstrate an understanding of concepts such as roles, status, and social class in describing the interactions of individuals and social groups.
	Analyze group and institutional influences on people, events, and elements of culture.
	Describe the various forms institutions take and the interactions of people with institutions.
	Identify and analyze examples of tensions between expressions of individuality and group or institutional efforts to promote social conformity.
	Identify and describe examples of tensions between belief systems and government policies and laws.
	Describe the role of institutions in furthering both continuity and change.
	Apply knowledge of how groups and institutions work to meet individual needs and promote the common good.
VI. Power, Authority, and Governance	Examine persistent issues involving the rights, roles, and status of the individual in relation to the general welfare.
	Describe the purpose of government and how its powers are acquired, used, and justified.
	Analyze and explain ideas and governmental mechanisms to meet needs and wants of citizens, regulate territory, manage conflict, and establish order and security.
	Describe the ways nations and organizations respond to forces of unity and diversity affecting order and security.
	Identify and describe the basic features of the political system in the United States, and identify representative leaders from various levels and branches of government.
	Explain conditions, actions, and motivations that contribute to conflict and cooperation within and among nations.
	Describe and analyze the roles of technology in communications, transportation, information processing, weapons development, or other areas as it contributes to or helps resolve conflicts.
	Explain and apply concepts such as power, role, status, justice, and influence to the examination of persistent issues and social problems.
	Give examples and explain how governments attempt to achieve their stated ideals at home and abroad.

VII. Production, Distribution, and Consumption	Describe a range of examples of the various institutions that make up economic systems such as households, business firms, banks, government agencies, labor unions, and corporations.
VIII. Science, Technology, and Society	
IX. Global Connections	Demonstrate an understanding of concerns, standards, issues, and conflicts related to universal human rights.
X. Civic Ideals and Practice	Examine the origins and continuing influence of key ideals of the democratic republican form of government, such as individual human dignity, liberty, justice, equality, and the rule of law.

Identify and interpret sources and examples of the rights and responsibilities of citizens.

Locate, access, analyze, organize, and apply information about selected public issues—recognizing and explaining multiple points of view.

Practice forms of civic discussions and participation consistent with the ideals of citizens in a democratic republic.

Identify and explain the roles of formal and informal political actors in influencing and shaping public policy and decision-making.

Analyze the influence of diverse forms of public opinion on the development of public policy and decision-making.

Analyze the effectiveness of selected public policies and citizen behaviors in realizing the stated ideals of a democratic republican form of government. |

Elections and Political Parties
in Brief

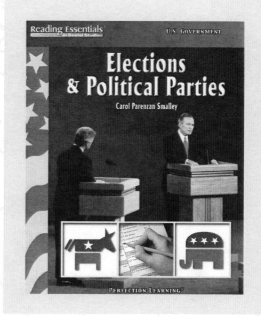

The United States government is a democracy where all citizens have the right to elect government leaders. The U.S. system of government has five levels: national, state, local, community, and the individual. The United Nations is a global organization to which many countries belong.

In the United States, registered voters can vote for their government officials. When citizens of the United States reach the age of 18, they can register to vote as Republicans, Democrats, or Independents. General elections are held every two years on the first Tuesday following the first Monday in November.

A candidate is someone who runs for political office. There are two types of candidates—recruited candidates, who are encouraged by other people to run for office, and self-starters, who make their own choice to enter politics. Abraham Lincoln is one of the most famous self-starters. Candidates reach the voters by scheduling debates, making home visits, advertising, holding rallies, and communicating via public relations departments.

Voting is one way that all U.S. citizens can contribute to their community and country. Today, all citizens—American-born or naturalized—can vote. Unfortunately, not everyone who can vote does. According to the Census Bureau for the 2000 presidential election, 86 percent of registered voters actually voted. Also in 2000, only 60 percent of citizens of voting age were registered to vote.

In the United States, voters do not vote directly for the candidates. Instead, they vote for electors who have promised to support these candidates. The electors make up a group called the Electoral College. The number of electors equals the number of senators and representatives each state sends to Congress. Today, there are 538 total electoral votes. A candidate needs 270 electoral votes to win.

A political party is a group of voters who share similar beliefs about government and important issues. There are currently two major political parties—Democrats and Republicans. The Democratic Party is the liberal party. This party wants states to have less power than the federal government. Republicans are thought to be more conservative in their approach to government and change. They want the federal government to be less involved, giving more power to the individual states.

U.S. citizens under the age of 18 may not be old enough to vote, but they can still be active members of their community, and they can still have a voice about issues facing the world. Studying current events and writing to political officials are ways young citizens can be involved. Fund-raising for social groups and being a friend to those in need are other ways. Everyone has the ability to make the world a better place.

Reading Exploration Essentials

Vocabulary

absentee balloting	affiliation	allocate	amendment
association	ballot	candidate	census
conservative	convention	debate	delegate
dictator	electoral	eligible	global
liberal	literacy	moderator	monarch
monarchy	naturalized	nominate	participatory
platform	poll tax	precinct	predetermined
primary election	public relations	rally	ratify
recall	referendum	right	self-starter
slogan	stand	suffrage	ticket

Reading Exploration

prereading

Discuss the timeline on pages 4–6 of *Elections and Political Parties*. Make a large copy of the timeline on butcher paper. Display it in the classroom. Have the students record each event in a notebook leaving ample space after each event.

during reading

As students read through the book, have them record interesting details or facts about each important event in their notebooks in the space provided.

postreading

Assign each student or pair of students one of the events on the timeline. Have them design a poster on a large sheet of construction paper depicting the given event with the date prominently featured. Using heavy string and clothespins, organize the pictures and hang the finished timeline in the classroom or hallway.

It's a Match!

Match each vocabulary word to its definition. Use the glossary in *Elections and Political Parties* if you need help.

_____	1. addition or change to a bill or the Constitution	a. ballot
_____	2. someone who acts as a mediator in debates	b. moderator
_____	3. leader who rules a country with absolute power, usually by force	c. nominate
_____	4. publicly announced policies and promises of a party seeking election	d. candidate
_____	5. to suggest someone for appointment or election	e. debate
_____	6. piece of paper or card on which someone can record a vote	f. amendment
_____	7. someone chosen to represent or given the authority to act on behalf of another person or group	g. delegate
_____	8. the right to vote in public elections	h. platform
_____	9. organized discussion of opinions or ideas	i. dictator
_____	10. someone who runs for election	j. suffrage

◎ **One Step Further:** Write the vocabulary words in alphabetical order below.

11. _____   16. _____

12. _____   17. _____

13. _____   18. _____

14. _____   19. _____

15. _____   20. _____

Instant Recall

Using your book, write a complete sentence to answer each question about *Elections and Political Parties*.

1. When is Election Day?

   _____

2. What is the minimum voting age in the United States?

   _____

3. What does the word *democracy* mean?

   _____

4. How often is a new governor elected?

   _____

5. Where is the first caucus in the election process held?

   _____

6. Where is the first primary in the election process held?

   _____

7. How many electoral votes does a candidate need to win a presidential election?

   _____

8. How many electoral votes does your state have?

   _____

9. What is the unofficial Democratic mascot?

   _____

10. What does GOP stand for?

   _____

An Opinion Poll

A fact is something proven to be true. An opinion is one person's personal feelings about a subject. Write a fact sentence and an opinion sentence for each topic listed below. The first one is done for you.

The Salary of the President of the United States

1. Fact   The U.S. president receives a salary of $400,000 per year.

   Opinion   The president of the United States makes a lot of money.

The Salary of a New York City Firefighter

2. Fact   _____

   Opinion   _____

Registering to Vote

3. Fact   _____

   Opinion   _____

Abraham Lincoln

4. Fact   _____

   Opinion   _____

The Voting Rights of Prisoners

5. Fact   _____

   Opinion   _____

Kids Voting in the United States

6. Fact   _____

   Opinion   _____

continued

An Opinion Poll *continued*

The 2000 Presidential Election

7. Fact _____

   Opinion _____

The Electoral College

8. Fact _____

   Opinion _____

The Democratic Party

9. Fact _____

   Opinion _____

The Republican Party

10. Fact _____

    Opinion _____

◎ **One Step Further:** Write a short paragraph with at least three details supporting one of the opinions you mentioned above. Use your opinion statement as the main idea sentence of your paragraph.

_____

_____

_____

_____

_____

Dear Mr. President

Write a letter to the president of the United States. Tell him about yourself. Thank him for his leadership. Explain what you like and dislike about decisions he has made. Share with him your concerns about the country. Ask him any questions you might have about his job or the welfare of the United States.

Use the format below for writing a friendly letter.

Send your letter to: The President of the United States
1600 Pennsylvania Avenue, NW
Washington, DC 20500

Heading
first line: street number and street name
second line: city, state, and ZIP code
third line: date

Greeting
Dear Mr. President,

Body
This is the main part of the letter. Include an introduction. The body explains why you're writing. Begin a new paragraph and indent each time you change the topic you're talking about. Be sure to add a conclusion at the end. The body is the longest part of the letter.

Closing
Choose an appropriate closing, and sign your name.

America Votes

Use the information in the table below to complete the graph. Draw points for each of the years. Connect the points to form a line graph. A line graph shows change over time.

Percentage of U.S. Population That Voted Each Year	
year	percentage
1964	61.9
1968	60.8
1972	55.2
1976	53.5
1980	52.5
1984	53.1
1988	50.1
1992	55.2
1996	49.08
2000	51.6

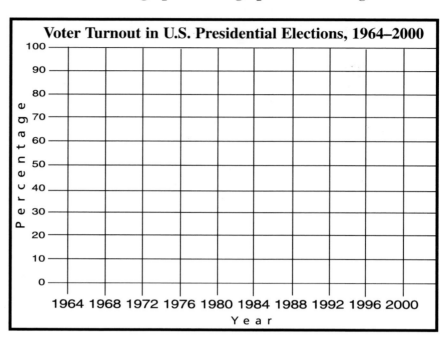

Voter Turnout in U.S. Presidential Elections, 1964–2000

◎ **One Step Further:** After looking at your graph, what conclusions can you draw about voters in America? What trends do you see?

_____

_____

_____

_____

_____

_____

_____

Project Ideas

Choose from the following project suggestions to show what you have learned about elections and political parties. You may want to work with a partner or in a small group. Share your finished project with your classmates.

- Hold an election for a class president. First choose two candidates. Assign a campaign manager and speechwriter for each candidate. Spend a couple of weeks campaigning, and then hold your election.

- Watch political shows on TV. Keep a log including the date of the broadcast and a summary of the news item. Do you agree or disagree with the views given? Chart at least five entries.

- On a large piece of posterboard, create a chart showing the five levels of government and the leaders we have elected. Include the leaders in your state and at your local and community levels.

- Make a poster advertising the importance of voting. Ask a local business to display your poster prior to an election.

- Invite your town mayor or a local politician to be a guest speaker in your classroom. Find out a few facts about the speaker and use them to write an introduction to the presentation.

- Organize a community service project such as reading to students in a younger class, raking leaves or shoveling snow for the elderly in your community, or picking up garbage at a nearby park. Keep a journal of your activities.

- Make a large map of the United States. On each state, write the number of electoral votes each state has been given. Make a worksheet to go with your map. Challenge another class or classmate to complete the worksheet using your map.

- Research and role-play Elizabeth Cady Stanton. As Stanton, share with the class your beliefs, thoughts, and dreams about women's rights.

- Analyze a campaign speech. You can watch a televised speech by a candidate running for local, state, or national office or read a published speech. How did you feel after listening to or reading the speech? Do you agree or disagree with the issues discussed? Would you feel comfortable supporting this candidate? Write a summary of your feelings.

- Stage a debate between two candidates. Select two students to be the candidates. Form two groups to help each candidate prepare for the debate. Following the debate, vote on the issue.

©Perfection Learning®

Twenty-Question Objective Test

Directions: Match each word and its meaning.

_____ 1. census

a. official count of the population that is done every ten years

_____ 2. debate

b. short catchy phrase used to identify something or someone

_____ 3. global

c. organized discussion of opinions or ideas

_____ 4. platform

d. relating to or happening throughout the whole world

_____ 5. slogan

e. publicly announced policies and promises of a party seeking election

---

Directions: Answer each statement True (T) or False (F).

_____ 6. Election Day is in December.

_____ 7. When U.S. citizens reach the age of 18, they can register to vote.

_____ 8. Voters who cannot physically go to their polling locations are not able to vote.

_____ 9. The president and vice president run for election on one ticket.

_____ 10. The Democratic Party is the conservative party.

Directions: Choose the best answer to complete each statement.

11. The 19th Amendment to the Constitution
    a. gives women the right to vote.
    b. prohibits states from collecting poll taxes.
    c. prohibits states from denying citizens a vote because of race, color, or prior history as a slave.

12. The word *democracy* means
    a. "government by the people."
    b. "ruled by dictators."
    c. "to form a perfect union."

continued

Elections and Political Parties

Twenty-Question Objective Test continued

13. Abraham Lincoln was one of the most famous
    a. Democrats.
    b. recruited candidates.
    c. self-starters.

14. The first primary in the presidential election is held in
    a. New York.
    b. New Hampshire.
    c. Iowa.

15. Giving all citizens the right to vote took
    a. 50 years.
    b. 200 years.
    c. 350 years.

16. Ballots in which voters filled in shapes next to the candidates' names were called
    a. punch cards.
    b. paper ballots.
    c. marksense ballots.

17. Today, there are a total of
    a. 538 electoral votes.
    b. 652 electoral votes.
    c. 770 electoral votes.

18. The first president of the United States was a
    a. Democrat.
    b. Republican.
    c. Federalist.

19. The donkey symbolizes the
    a. Democratic Party.
    b. Republican Party.
    c. Federalist Party.

continued

Elections and Political Parties
Twenty-Question Objective Test continued

Directions: Answer the question using complete sentences.

20. You are not old enough to vote, but you can be an active member of your community. What can you do to contribute in your community and to voice your opinion about issues facing you and your world?

_____

_____

_____

_____

_____

_____

_____

_____

_____

_____

_____

_____

_____

_____

_____

_____

_____

_____

_____

_____

The Executive Branch
in Brief

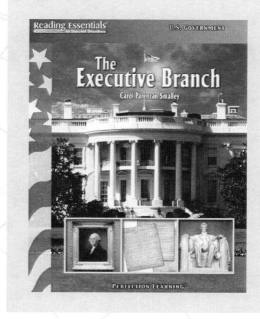

The history of the United States government began in the early 1600s. The colonists were discontent with the British monarchy and fought for freedom. This march for independence led to the founding of the United States of America. In 1787, the new country crafted the Constitution of the United States, guidelines for the new government. The Constitution is still used today.

The executive branch is one of three branches of the government. It ensures that the laws of the United States are obeyed. The president of the United States is the head of the executive branch. Other members include the vice president, the cabinet, the Executive Office, and independent agencies.

The president depends on the members of his cabinet to advise him. Cabinet members are selected at the beginning of the president's term and must be approved by the Senate. Cabinet departments such as Agriculture, Defense, Education, Justice, and Homeland Security present information and options to the president to help him in his daily work.

The president needs a strong staff to organize and guide him. This staff is called the Executive Office. Most of the offices, councils, and boards within the Executive Office were created by executive order or by acts of Congress. The National Security Council, the Office of Administration, the USA Freedom Corps, and the White House Military Office are just a few of the staff groups.

In addition to the president's cabinet and Executive Office agencies and councils, the executive branch also includes independent agencies. Congress created the independent agencies to advise the president about specific concerns. Some of them include the Central Intelligence Agency, the Commission on Civil Rights, the Environmental Protection Agency, and the Equal Employment Opportunity Commission.

The creators of the Constitution established a government that has persevered for more than 225 years. The United States has more than tripled in size since 1776. The three branches of government—the executive branch, the legislative branch, and the judicial branch—continue to work together to maintain a well-balanced government.

Reading Exploration Essentials

Vocabulary

amend	checks and balances	confirmed	discontent
domestic	entrepreneur	executive branch	executive order
formal	impeachment	implied	impoverished
judicial branch	jurisdiction	legislative branch	obstruction of justice
perjury	policy	preamble	precedent
resign	succeed	sworn in	ticket
transportation	veteran	veto	

Reading Exploration

prereading

Ask the students what they know about the executive branch of government. Explain to them that there are three branches of government—executive, legislative, and judicial. This book will be covering the executive branch, which is headed by the president.

On a large sheet of paper, build a word web with the president of the United States as the focus. Find out what the students know about the job of the president. Add their details to the web.

during reading

Have the students make brief outlines as they read through each chapter. Tell them to write down any important or interesting information.

postreading

Put the students in small groups. Using their outlines, have each group create a new web for the president of the United States. Have a spokesperson from each group share the web with the rest of the class.

Executive Branch Crossword

Read the sentences about the executive branch below. Use the words in the box to fill in the vocabulary word that is missing in each one. Then put the words where they belong in the crossword puzzle on page 30. You will not use all the words.

amend	confirmed	discontent	domestic
formal	impeachment	implied	jurisdiction
perjury	policy	precedent	resign
succeed	ticket	veteran	veto

Across

1. In order to change a law, lawmakers must _____ the Constitution.

2. The executive branch wanted senators to discuss the bill, but that action was outside
   of its _____.

3. What is the school's _____ about wearing hats?

4. The attorney argued for her client using a _____ set in another case.

5. In 2000, Albert Gore was hoping to _____ William J. Clinton
   as president.

6. My grandfather is a _____ of World War II.

Down

7. The congressman committed _____ when he lied under oath.

8. The Senate plays a large role in the _____ process.

9. According to the 25th Amendment, the president can nominate a vice president,
   but he or she must be _____ by Congress before taking office.

10. The departments of Health and Human Services and Homeland Security
    are _____ agencies because they deal with internal affairs of
    the United States.

continued

Executive Branch Crossword *continued*

11. President Nixon chose to _____ from office rather than go through the impeachment process.

12. The colonists were _____ with British rule, so they fought for their freedom.

◎ **One Step Further:** Use the four glossary words remaining in the box. Show that you understand the meaning of each word by using it in a sentence.

1. _____

2. _____

3. _____

4. _____

Ordering the Facts

Read the three groups of sentences below. Number the sentences in order.

Group 1

_____ Citizens of Great Britain sailed across the Atlantic Ocean.

_____ The United States of America was founded.

_____ The citizens established colonies along the eastern coast of the North American continent.

_____ The new colonies were ruled by the British monarchy.

_____ The colonists decided to fight for their freedom.

Group 2

_____ The Senate found the president guilty.

_____ The House voted in favor of impeachment.

_____ The people felt that the president had done something wrong.

_____ The president was removed from office.

_____ The impeachment process began.

Group 3

_____ President George W. Bush wanted to protect our nation against additional threats.

_____ This group of agencies became the Department of Homeland Security.

_____ President George W. Bush brought together the separate domestic agencies.

_____ Terrorists attacked America on September 11.

_____ The Department of Homeland Security developed a terrorist alert color code system.

Sticking with the Main Idea

Read each paragraph below. Draw a line through the sentence that does not belong. Then choose the main idea of the paragraph from the choices given.

1. According to the Constitution, the vice president has two primary duties. He presides over the Senate, but he does not debate or vote, except in the case of a tie. The vice president also steps in when the president is disabled or unable to perform his duties. The vice president's office is in the West Wing of the White House.

   a. The vice president has two main jobs.

   b. The vice president does not normally debate or vote unless there is a tie.

   c. The vice president takes the president's place if he becomes disabled.

2. Many presidents and their families enjoyed pets. Siamese cats were popular prowlers around the White House. John Quincy Adams kept an alligator in the house. James Buchanan had an elephant. Ulysses S. Grant made room for a couple of pigs. Camp David is a popular vacation spot for the president. Calvin Coolidge even had a hippo!

   a. There have been several Siamese cats around the White House.

   b. Ulysses S. Grant had pet pigs.

   c. Many different types of animals have called the White House home.

3. The Department of Interior oversees memorial sites in Washington, D.C. The Justice Department was established in 1870. Since 1870, the department has grown into the largest law office in the country. It is responsible for enforcing all federal laws. It also provides the president and other department heads with legal advice.

   a. Federal laws are enforced by the Justice Department.

   b. The Justice Department plays an important role in the legal system of the United States.

   c. The Justice Department has grown since it was established in 1870.

continued

©Perfection Learning®

Sticking with the Main Idea *continued*

4. For some, child labor was more than just doing chores. Instead of going to school, some children spent their day working in a factory for minimal pay. Their families needed them to work to earn money. The Department of State is the oldest cabinet department. The conditions in many of the factories were horrendous. There are currently laws to prevent young children from working, putting their education first.

   a. Children used to be factory workers.

   b. Education is important for children.

   c. Although child labor was once a way of life for some families, it is now illegal.

5. The National Security Council is the president's main forum for discussing national security issues with senior national-security advisors and cabinet officials. President George W. Bush created the Office of Faith-Based and Community Initiatives in 2001. Because of its importance, the council is chaired by the president himself. Members of the council include the vice president, the secretary of state, the secretary of the treasury, the secretary of defense, and the assistant to the president for National Security Affairs.

   a. The National Security Council discusses issues of national security and includes the president and several senior White House officials.

   b. The president chairs the National Security Council.

   c. One member of the National Security Council is the secretary of state.

◎ **One Step Further:** On another sheet of paper, rewrite one of the paragraphs above. Omit the sentence that does not belong and add at least two more supporting details.

A Presidential Biography

A biography is a written history of a person's life. Research a past president of the United States. Use the questions below to guide you in your research. On a separate sheet of paper, organize your information into a biography.

Which president have you chosen?

When did he hold office?

What political party was he affiliated with?

Describe his childhood and upbringing.

What type of education did he receive?

Describe his family.

What major events happened while he was in office?

If he is deceased, how did he die? If he is living, what is he currently doing?

Describe your feelings about this president.

◎ **One Step Further:** Draw a portrait of the president to accompany your biography.

Reading a Timeline

A timeline shows important events in history. Use the timeline below to answer the questions about the executive branch of the government.

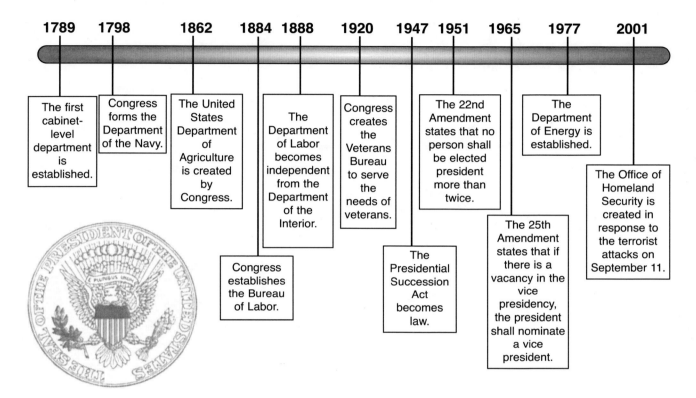

1. When did the Department of Labor become independent from the Department of the Interior?

_____

2. When did Congress form the Department of the Navy?

_____

3. What amendment to the Constitution was added in 1951?

_____

continued

Reading a Timeline *continued*

4. How much time elapsed between the adding of the 22nd Amendment and the 25th Amendment?

   _____

5. What office was created in 2001?

   _____

6. When did the Presidential Succession Act become law?

   _____

7. What's the shortest time span shown on the timeline?

   _____

◎ **One Step Further:** Add three more dates and events to the timeline.

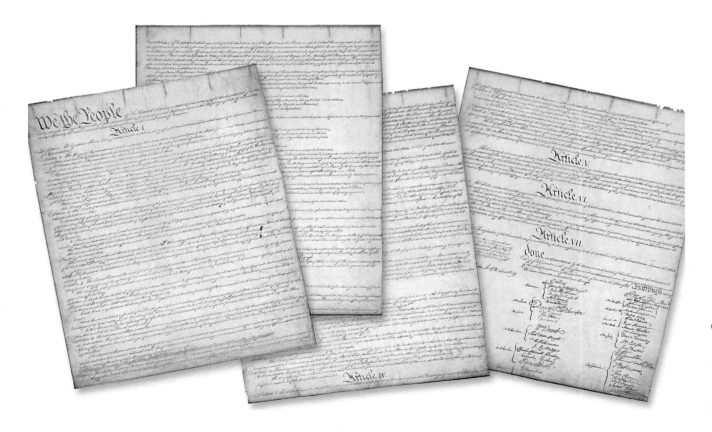

Project Ideas

Choose from the following project suggestions to show what you have learned about the executive branch. You may want to work with a partner or in a small group. Share your finished project with your classmates.

◎ Write a play reenacting the major events of the American Revolutionary War.

◎ Draw a map of the White House.

◎ Research a first lady. Write a report to summarize your findings.

◎ Write a paragraph on your opinion about electing a woman as president of the United States.

◎ Write a poem symbolizing your feelings about the September 11 terrorist attacks on the United States.

◎ Find out more about the "No Child Left Behind Act." Interview your local administrator to see how your school has been affected. Share your findings with your class.

◎ Design a poster showing the Homeland Security Advisory System.

◎ Make a travel brochure for one of the presidential memorial sites in Washington, D.C.

◎ Become a member of the USA Freedom Corps by volunteering your time. You can read to younger children, organize a used-toy drive at your school, or help an elderly neighbor. Share your experience with your class.

◎ Collect pictures of Air Force One from magazines or the Internet. Make a collage to display in your classroom. Add interesting facts you discovered during your research.

Twenty-Question Objective Test

Directions: Match each word and its meaning.

_____ 1. amend

_____ 2. domestic

_____ 3. jurisdiction

_____ 4. policy

_____ 5. succeed

a. to follow somebody occupying a post or position

b. to revise or alter something

c. program of actions

d. power or right to exercise control

e. relating to the internal affairs of a nation

Directions: Answer each statement True (T) or False (F).

_____ 6. The Constitution is a document that sets the principles guiding our nation.

_____ 7. The president is the head of the executive branch of government.

_____ 8. Anyone who is at least 35 years old can run for president of the United States.

_____ 9. The members of the cabinet are explained in the Constitution.

_____ 10. The Department of Homeland Security was created in response to the terrorist attacks of September 11.

Directions: Choose the best answer to complete each statement.

11. The war against Great Britain is referred to as
    a. World War II.
    b. the Civil War.
    c. the American Revolutionary War.

12. The three equal branches of the U.S. government are the
    a. conservative, executive, and governmental branches.
    b. objective, corrective, and executive branches.
    c. executive, legislative, and judicial branches.

continued

©Perfection Learning®

The Executive Branch

Twenty-Question Objective Test continued

13. If a president dies during his term, the
    a. vice president becomes the president.
    b. secretary of state becomes the president.
    c. people elect a new president.

14. The only president who didn't live in the White House was
    a. Abraham Lincoln.
    b. George Washington.
    c. John F. Kennedy.

15. The secret gathering of cabinet advisors was called the
    a. Executive Cabinet.
    b. Backdoor Cabinet.
    c. Kitchen Cabinet.

16. The Defense Department's building is the shape of a
    a. hexagon.
    b. pentagon.
    c. octagon.

17. The oldest cabinet department is the
    a. Department of State.
    b. Department of Labor.
    c. Department of Justice.

18. The president's main forum for discussing national security and foreign policy issues is called the
    a. Office of Administration.
    b. National Security Council.
    c. Department of Justice.

19. Since 1776, the Unites States has
    a. almost doubled in size.
    b. almost tripled in size.
    c. more than tripled in size.

continued

The Executive Branch
Twenty-Question Objective Test continued

Directions: Answer the question using complete sentences.

20. What are the powers of the president of the United States?
Name at least three.

_____

_____

_____

_____

_____

_____

_____

_____

_____

_____

_____

_____

_____

_____

_____

_____

The Judicial Branch
in Brief

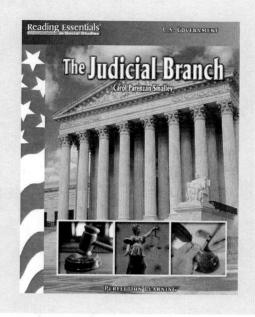

The Supreme Court heads the judicial branch, one of the three branches of the federal government. The judicial branch is responsible for interpreting the Constitution of the United States. In 1787, the U.S. Constitution established the Supreme Court. The number of justices serving on the Supreme Court has changed throughout history, but since 1869, there have been nine justices.

The most important job of the Supreme Court is to interpret the U.S. Constitution. The Court decides if a law or action by the government violates the Constitution. In a typical year, the Court hears fewer than 100 cases. In addition to hearing cases, the Court may rule on cases involving foreign dignitaries, maritime disputes, and national crises.

There are no official qualifications for Supreme Court justices. They are appointed by the president and must be approved by the Senate. Supreme Court justices serve life terms, but can be impeached if they commit a high crime or misdemeanor.

The faces of the Supreme Court have changed throughout history. Louis Brandeis became the first Jewish justice in 1916. In 1967, Lyndon B. Johnson appointed the first African American justice, Thurgood Marshall. Sandra Day O'Connor became the first female justice in 1982.

There are many people who work behind the scenes at the Supreme Court. Each justice can have up to four assistants. They research and read petitions put before the Court. The Court has two attorneys, known as the Legal Office. They handle the Court's legal concerns. Over 200 security officers work in or on the grounds of the Supreme Court Building. There is a director of data systems, and the chief justice has an administrative assistant. A reporter records all opinions and decisions, a public information officer handles the press, and a librarian manages the Court's library.

The Supreme Court did not have its own building until 1935. The Supreme Court Building is located in Washington, D.C. Architect Cass Gilbert designed the building.

Attorneys presenting cases to the Supreme Court usually take about one hour to argue the case. After hearing the case, the justices discuss it privately. They then take a preliminary vote. All opinions written up are carefully reviewed before announcing the decision based on a majority vote. The Court meets from the first Monday of October until June.

Many of the Supreme Court's decisions have changed the course of American history with issues such as slavery, race segregation, freedom of speech, and affirmative action.

The Supreme Court is rich in its tradition and history. The cases that the Court hears year after year help shape the future of the United States of America.

Reading Exploration Essentials

Vocabulary

administrative case	appeal	associate justice	bench
bill	borked	chief justice	civil case
clerk	concurring opinion	Court of Appeals	criminal case
defendant	dissenting opinion	district court	docket
executive branch	federal	federal judicial district	grant cert
impeachment	judicial branch	judicial review	judicial system
justice	legal brief	Legal Office	legislative branch
litigants	majority opinion	opinion	oral argument
Orders List	oyez	pauper petition	petition
plaintiff	seniority	Supreme Court	term
writ of certiorari			

Reading Exploration

prereading

Examine and discuss a diagram of the three branches of government. Explain to the students that they will be reading about the judicial branch of government. Ask the students if they know anything about the judicial branch. Where is it housed? Who makes up the judicial branch? What are its duties and primary responsibilities?

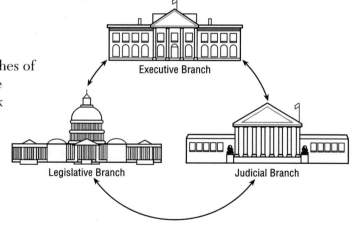

Executive Branch

Legislative Branch

Judicial Branch

during reading

Have the students keep a brief outline as they read through the book. Explain to them how to organize their notes with headings and details. Ask them to listen for details to add to the prereading discussion. Remind them that when taking notes, they do not need to write complete sentences. They need to only jot down important details and facts.

postreading

Divide the students into small groups. Give each group a chapter to summarize and present to the class. Have them refer to their notes for important information.

The Word in Government

Read the pronunciations and definitions below. Write the vocabulary word from *The Judicial Branch* that matches.

1. _____ (puh TISH uhn) written request for the Court to hear a case

2. _____ (dee FEN duhnt) individual or organization accused of violating a civil or private right in a civil case or of committing a crime in a criminal case

3. _____ (uh PEEL) request to take a lower court's decision to a higher court for review

4. _____ (JUS tis) member of the Supreme Court

5. _____ (seen YOR uh tee) ordered according to years of experience, from most experienced to least experienced

6. _____ (DOK et) group of cases the Court is planning to hear

7. _____ (FED uh ruhl) of or relating to the U.S. government

8. _____ (PLAYN tif) individual or organization making a complaint in a lawsuit

9. _____ (oh PIN yuhn) decision made by the Court

10. _____ (LIT uh guhnts) plaintiffs and defendants

◎ **One Step Further:** Put the above answers in alphabetical order.

11. _____   16. _____

12. _____   17. _____

13. _____   18. _____

14. _____   19. _____

15. _____   20. _____

Expressing Yourself

Read through the following Supreme Court landmark decisions. Do you agree or disagree with the Court's decisions? Write your opinion on the lines below each case. Use details to support your opinion.

Dred Scott v. Sandford (1856)

Dred Scott was a slave in Missouri. He asked the state of Missouri to free him and his wife from slavery because he had traveled with his master to "free territories." Scott claimed that his residence in a free territory made him a free man. But the Missouri Supreme Court disagreed. Scott remained a slave.

The United States Supreme Court upheld the decision of the Missouri Supreme Court. The Court decided that slaves were property and not citizens with rights. Scott remained a slave.

Do you agree or disagree with the Supreme Court's decision?

_____

_____

_____

Tinker v. Des Moines Independent School District (1969)

Three Des Moines school students decided to protest the Vietnam War by wearing black armbands to school. School officials asked the students to remove the bands or face suspension. The students refused and were suspended.

The Court ruled that the First Amendment protected the right to wear armbands. The Court believed that the school officials lacked justification for imposing the limitation of the bands. They failed to show that that the wearing of the bands would interfere with an appropriate school environment.

Do you agree or disagree with the Supreme Court's decision?

_____

_____

_____

continued

Expressing Yourself *continued*

United States v. Eichman (1990)

In 1989, the Supreme Court decided in Texas v. Johnson that the Texas law making flag burning illegal was unconstitutional. Then Congress passed the Flag Protection Act because it disagreed with the Supreme Court's decision in Texas v. Johnson. The Act made it a crime to destroy an American flag or any likeness of an American flag that was "commonly displayed." Several prosecutions resulted from the Act.

The Court overturned the law. It felt that it limited an individual's right to free expression.

Do you agree or disagree with the Supreme Court's final decision?

_____

_____

_____

An Eye for an Eye

The expression "an eye for an eye, a tooth for a tooth" comes from the 282 laws known as Hammurabi's Code. Violators of the Code were brought before judges. Their actions often resulted in harsh penalties. Review the sidebar on page 12 of *The Judicial Branch*. Think of the actions as the *causes* and the penalties as the *effects*. Pair the causes below with their effects.

Cause

_____ 1. A man steals a goat that belongs to the court.

_____ 2. A man steals a goat that belongs to a freed man of the king.

_____ 3. A man puts out the eye of another man.

_____ 4. A man is caught committing a robbery.

_____ 5. A son strikes his father.

Effect

a. The son's hands are hewn off.

b. The thief has to pay thirtyfold.

c. The man is put to death.

d. The man has to pay tenfold.

e. The man's eye is put out.

Causes and effects can also been seen in our modern-day judicial system. Pair the following causes with their effects.

Cause

_____ 6. An individual violates a federal law.

_____ 7. An individual thinks the regulations are unfair.

_____ 8. There is a national crisis.

_____ 9. A Supreme Court justice opposes Louis Brandeis's appointment.

_____ 10. A lawyer is given a white light.

Effect

f. The Supreme Court is called into an emergency session.

g. The lawyer has permission to speak.

h. The individual is called into court to defend his actions.

i. The Supreme Court justice refuses to sit next to Brandeis.

j. The individual asks the federal judge to hear the case and determine the fairness of the regulations.

Supreme Court Justices

You are a reporter for a legal magazine, and your job is to write an informative report about becoming a Supreme Court justice. Remember that a good paragraph has one main idea. The other sentences in the paragraph should support the main idea. Use this page as a guide for organizing your paragraphs. Then write your final draft on a separate piece of paper.

What qualifications are needed to become a Supreme Court justice?

Main idea sentence

_____

_____

Supporting details

_____

_____

_____

_____

_____

How is a Supreme Court justice appointed?

Main idea sentence

_____

_____

Supporting details

_____

_____

_____

_____

_____

continued

Supreme Court Justices *continued*

How is a Supreme Court justice removed from office?

Main idea sentence

_____

_____

Supporting details

_____

_____

_____

_____

◉ **One Step Further:** Who are the justices currently serving on the Supreme Court?

_____

_____

_____

_____

_____

Supreme Court Building

Work together as a class to make an exterior model of the Supreme Court Building. Look closely at several detailed photographs of the Supreme Court Building. Each small group should concentrate on creating a section of the building. Using various materials (such as toothpicks, clay, marshmallows, sugar cubes, and cardboard), construct a version of the Supreme Court Building. Be creative in your use of materials. Try to include as many of the following details as possible.

- the sixteen marble columns

- the portico and the motto

- the nine sculpted figures representing important people involved in the building's creation

- the two marble figures on either side of the main entrance

- the marble figures on the east entrance representing the great lawgivers

- the bronze doors

Project Ideas

Choose from the following project suggestions to show what you have learned about the judicial branch of government. You may want to work with a partner or in a small group. Share your finished project with your classmates.

◎ Who currently serves on the Supreme Court? Write a biography on one of the current justices. Include a photograph or sketch of the justice.

◎ Hold a mock trial of a case that was heard by the Supreme Court.

◎ Hammurabi's Code consists of 282 laws. You read about 4 of them in *The Judicial Branch*. Research the Code and write down at least 20 more laws. How do you feel about the fairness of these laws? Include your opinion in a paragraph at the bottom of your page.

◎ Create a bulletin board display of the judicial branch for your classroom.

◎ Imagine you are a young African American child in the 1940s. The schools are all segregated. How do you feel about segregation according to race? How do you feel about not being permitted to attend the school for white children?

◎ Compare and contrast the three branches of government. Prepare a presentation with the information you have gathered.

◎ Create a "Political Jeopardy" game. Use the vocabulary words and other important information from *The Judicial Branch*. Make up a series of answers and questions. Here are two examples.

> Answer: Justice.
> Question: What is a member of the Supreme Court called?

> Answer: Sandra Day O'Connor.
> Question: Who was the first woman to serve on the Supreme Court?

◎ Research one of the "Supreme Court Firsts" in more detail. Write a report to summarize your findings.

◎ Design a brochure educating the reader about the judicial branch of government.

◎ Write a proposal for a student court at your school. What types of cases would the court hear? What types of punishment would be recommended to the principal? Develop a list of court procedures and a process for the selection of student judges.

Twenty-Question Objective Test

Directions: Match each word and its meaning.

_____ 1. appeal

_____ 2. docket

_____ 3. federal

_____ 4. justice

_____ 5. petition

a. group of cases the court is planning to hear

b. of or relating to the U.S. government

c. written request for the Court to hear a case

d. member of the Supreme Court

e. to take a lower court's decision to a higher court for review

Directions: Answer each statement True (T) or False (F).

_____ 6. The judicial branch is the most important branch of government.

_____ 7. The judicial review is at the head of the federal judicial branch.

_____ 8. The Supreme Court can be called into an emergency session if there is a national crisis.

_____ 9. A Supreme Court justice does not have to be an attorney.

_____ 10. There are ten justices on the Supreme Court.

Directions: Choose the best answer to complete each statement.

11. The Supreme Court Building is currently located in
    a. Washington, D.C.
    b. New York City.
    c. Dallas, Texas.

12. A Supreme Court justice serves a term of
    a. four years.
    b. nine years.
    c. life.

continued

The Judicial Branch
Twenty-Question Objective Test continued

13. The Supreme Court was established by the U.S. Constitution in
    a. 1787.
    b. 1817.
    c. 1852.

14. A case involving rules set by one of the government agencies is called
    a. a civil case.
    b. an administrative case.
    c. a criminal case.

15. A new Supreme Court justice is appointed by the president but must be approved by the
    a. voters of America.
    b. House of Representatives.
    c. Senate.

16. The first African American justice was
    a. Samuel Chase.
    b. Thurgood Marshall.
    c. Louis Brandeis.

17. If an attorney sees a red light when presenting his case, he must
    a. begin to summarize his presentation.
    b. stop his presentation.
    c. leave the courtroom.

18. A majority is
    a. more than half.
    b. less than half.
    c. at least half.

19. Jim Crow was a
    a. famous black slave.
    b. Supreme Court Justice.
    c. way of life for African Americans.

continued

The Judicial Branch
Twenty-Question Objective Test continued

Directions: Answer the question using complete sentences.

20. In your own words, summarize one of the landmark decisions that shaped Supreme Court history.

_____

_____

_____

_____

_____

_____

_____

_____

_____

_____

_____

_____

_____

_____

_____

_____

The Legislative Branch
in Brief

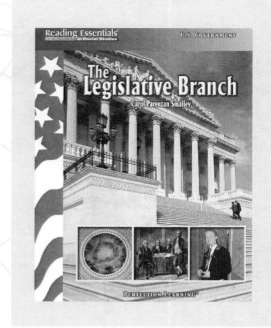

The United States government has three branches—executive, legislative, and judicial. This book focuses on the legislative branch. The legislative branch is headed by Congress, which is made up of the Senate and the House of Representatives.

Each state has two senators. A senator serves a six-year term. The number of representatives in each state depends on the state's population. There are 435 seats in the House. Each state is guaranteed one representative, and the remaining seats are divided according to each state's population. Representatives serve two-year terms.

When the Founders of the United States created the U.S. Constitution, they strove for balance within the federal government. They created three separate but equally balanced branches of the government. The executive branch carries out the country's laws. The judicial branch interprets the country's laws. And the legislative branch creates the country's laws.

Candidates for both the U.S. Senate and the House of Representatives must be citizens of the United States. They must also live in the state they represent. In addition, in order to be elected to a seat in the Senate, or upper chamber, the candidate must be at least 30 years old and have lived in the country at least nine years. Once elected, there are no limits as to the number of terms a senator may serve. Representatives, on the other hand, need only be at least 25 years old. They must have lived in the United States a minimum of seven years. Like senators, there are no term limits.

Washington, D.C, the nation's capital, serves as the center of government. The building where the legislators meet is the called the Capitol Building. It is located along the Potomac River.

Inside the Capitol Building is the Senate chamber, where senators meet to focus on issues of national interest. Representatives meet in the House chamber. They concentrate on issues at the state and local level, along with financial issues.

Congress's primary job is to write laws for the country and to change laws that are no longer working well. Before an idea is presented and becomes a law, it is known as a bill. A bill must be approved by both the House and the Senate. It then goes to the president. The president can either sign it or veto it. If he signs it, it becomes a law. If he vetoes it, it goes back to the House and the Senate for another vote. Congress can override a president's veto if two-thirds of both Senators and Representatives agree.

In addition to making laws, the U.S. Constitution says that only Congress can declare war. It has only declared war five times in history. Congress is also responsible for the nation's budget.

The Founders of the United States believed that all citizens had the right to a voice in government. Today, each voice is heard through the country's elected representatives. Each branch of the nation's government works in unison with the others to create a balance of power.

Reading Exploration Essentials

Vocabulary

amendment	apportionment	bill	capital
capitol	chamber	Congress	congressional district
congresspeople	Continental Congress	deficit	electoral votes
federal holiday	filibuster	floor	hearing
House of Representatives	impeachment	joint committee	joint session
legislator	lobbyist	majority party	minority party
president pro tempore	redistricting	representative	select *or* special committee
Senate	senator	Speaker of the House	standing committee
succession	table	term	unconstitutional
veto	whips		

Reading Exploration

prereading

On a classroom map or globe, find Washington, D.C., and discuss its location. Pose these questions to students. How far is Washington, D.C., from where you live? What bodies of water are nearby? What states border Washington, D.C.? What do you already know about Washington, D.C.?

Explain to the students that there are three branches of U.S. government—the executive branch, the judicial branch, and the legislative branch.

Create a K-W-L chart to guide reading.

Know

Explain that the legislative branch is made up of Congress, which consists of senators and representatives. Ask students what they already know about the country's senators and representatives. Write their answers in the K section of the K-W-L chart.

Want to learn

Ask the students what they would like to learn about the senators and representatives that make up the nation's legislative branch of government. Record their questions in the W section.

during reading

Encourage students to continue adding questions to the K-W-L chart as they read.

postreading

Learned

With the students, refer to the lists of questions that were recorded in the K-W-L chart. Which questions are they now able to answer? Record the students' answers on the L section of the chart. Encourage students to find the answers to remaining questions.

Hearing Double

Some words have multiple meanings. For example, a table is a piece of furniture, but it also means to put something aside for later discussion. The words in the box have more than one meaning. Use the words to complete the sentences below. You will use each word more than once.

bill	floor
capital	hearing
chamber	whip

1. Each part, or _____, of Congress has similar responsibilities.

2. The man handed the salesperson a dollar _____.

3. The _____ choir sang for the president.

4. The rider cracked his _____, and the horses began trotting.

5. The _____ is the city that serves as the center of government.

6. A _____ was held to discuss the bill.

7. The senator was not sure he was _____ the president correctly.

8. A duck has a _____.

9. The representative stood on the round _____ of the rotunda.

10. Before an idea is passed or becomes a law, it is known as a _____.

11. The _____ is the main level in the House or Senate chambers.

12. Proper nouns begin with _____ letters.

13. An individual who works to gain passing votes is called a _____.

continued

©Perfection Learning®

Hearing Double *continued*

◎ **One Step Further:** Which word did you use more than twice? _____

Use your dictionary to look up and write the three different definitions for this word that were used in the activity.

Definition #1

_____

_____

Definition #2

_____

_____

Definition #3

_____

_____

House vs. Senate

The Venn diagram on page 8 of *The Legislative Branch* shows similarities and differences between the House and the Senate. Use the diagram to answer the following questions.

1. How are the legislators of Congress similar?

   _____

   _____

   _____

2. How are the legislators of Congress different?

   _____

   _____

   _____

3. How are the functions of the House and the Senate similar?

   _____

   _____

   _____

4. How are the functions of the House and the Senate different?

   _____

   _____

   _____

◎ **One Step Further:** Who are the senators and representatives from your state?

   _____

   _____

©Perfection Learning®

Name _____

Congress Declares War

The United States Constitution says that only Congress can declare war. It has only declared war five times in history. Choose one of those historic battles from the list below. Read about it in a book, in an encyclopedia, or on the Internet. Write a paragraph summarizing the main details of the war.

The War of 1812
The U.S.-Mexican War
The Spanish-American War
World War I
World War II

You may want to use the following questions to help organize your notes.

1. Why did the U.S. become involved in this war?

   _____

   _____

2. How long did the war last?

   _____

   _____

3. Who were the president and other leaders at the time of the war?

   _____

   _____

4. What did the war accomplish?

   _____

   _____

5. Other interesting information:

   _____

   _____

   _____

continued

Congress Declares War *continued*

Summarizing Paragraph

_____

_____

_____

_____

_____

_____

_____

_____

_____

◎ **One Step Further:** Imagine that you are the president of the United States at the time of one of the five conflicts listed on page 59. Use the information you have gathered and write a speech that you will deliver to Congress. It is your responsibility to convince them to declare war. Give the speech to your class.

Conquering the Nation's Debt

Imagine you are an editor for your local or school newspaper. You will be writing an editorial on the U.S. national debt. A newspaper editorial is an article that expresses the opinion of the editor or publisher.

In January 2004, the nation's debt was almost seven trillion dollars. This debt has occurred because the nation has borrowed money to pay for expenses each year.

How do you feel about the nation's debt? What action should be taken to reduce it? Write an editorial expressing your opinions in the space below.

◎ **One Step Further:** Submit your editorial to your local or school newspaper.

A "Capital" Vacation Spot

Design a travel brochure for the nation's capital. Describe some of the exciting things to do and places to visit in Washington, D.C. Use bright colors, pictures, and catchy slogans to capture the reader's attention. You may want to look at samples of travel brochures from other places for ideas.

Start with a piece of white paper. Fold the paper into thirds. Design your brochure. Be sure it is clearly labeled. You may want to do additional research to find other tourist attractions in the area.

Use the box below to sketch ideas for your brochure.

©*Perfection Learning*®

Project Ideas

Choose from the following project suggestions to show what you have learned about the legislative branch of the government. You may want to work with a partner or in a small group. Share your finished project with your classmates.

◎ Find out more about one of the senators or representatives from your state. Write a biography on your chosen politician.

◎ Make a timeline showing the steps the United States took to achieve a balanced government.

◎ Tour the Capitol Building online at **www.senate.gov/vtour**. Write a journal entry describing your tour. What rooms did you find the most interesting?

◎ Learn the lyrics to Schoolhouse Rock's "I'm Just a Bill." Write a skit about how a bill becomes a law. Perform the skit and sing the song for your classmates.

◎ Research and write a report about one of the country's federal holidays.

◎ How does the United States' system of government compare to other governments throughout the world? Choose a country to research. Organize the information you find using a Venn diagram.

◎ Create a silhouette or shadow portrait of George Washington, the first president of the United States. Write five of Washington's major accomplishments in complete sentences on the back of your portrait.

◎ Make a class chart showing the first ten amendments to the Constitution and the rights that each one guarantees.

◎ Create a giant map of the number of representatives given to each state in the United States. Color-code your map. Identify the ten states with the highest numbers of representatives and the ten states with the lowest numbers of representatives.

◎ Write a new amendment you would like to see added to the Constitution. Include the reasons why you think the amendment is necessary.

Twenty-Question Objective Test

Directions: Match each word and its meaning.

_____ 1. capital   a. building in which legislators meet

_____ 2. capitol   b. individual who represents a certain interest or group

_____ 3. deficit   c. power or right to reject something

_____ 4. lobbyist   d. city that serves as the center of government

_____ 5. veto   e. result when spending is greater than earning

Directions: Answer each statement True (T) or False (F).

_____ 6. There are more representatives than there are senators.

_____ 7. The first Continental Congress met in Philadelphia.

_____ 8. The nation's capital does not belong to an individual state.

_____ 9. The House of Representatives approves presidential nominations.

_____ 10. Only the president of the United States can declare war.

Directions: Choose the best answer to complete each statement.

11. The number of United States senators is
    a. 100.
    b. 125.
    c. 235.

12. The number of United States representatives is
    a. 125.
    b. 435.
    c. 500.

continued

The Legislative Branch
Twenty-Question Objective Test continued

13. The capital city of the United States is
    a. Washington.
    b. Spokane, Washington.
    c. Washington, D.C.

14. U.S. representatives are elected every
    a. two years.
    b. five years.
    c. six years.

15. The nation's capital is nestled along the
    a. Mississippi River.
    b. Missouri River.
    c. Potomac River.

16. The rotunda is a/an
    a. oval-shaped office in the center of the Capitol.
    b. circular space in the center of the Capitol.
    c. pentagon-shaped building not far from the Capitol.

17. The leader of the members of the House is called the
    a. Senate Majority Leader.
    b. Speaker of the House.
    c. President Pro Tempore.

18. Before an idea is passed and becomes a law, it is called a/an
    a. bill.
    b. amendment.
    c. filibuster.

19. Amber Alert was named after
    a. a little girl who was kidnapped.
    b. the woman who created the tracking system.
    c. the flashing lights, which are amber-colored.

©Perfection Learning®

continued

The Legislative Branch
Twenty-Question Objective Test continued

Directions: Answer the question using complete sentences.

20. What are two similarities and two differences of the U.S. Senate and the U.S. House?

_____

_____

_____

_____

_____

_____

©Perfection Learning®

State and Local Government
in Brief

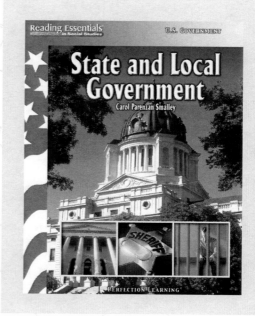

The government in the United States is based on a multilevel system—federal, state, county, city, and community. Each level has its own responsibilities, but they all work together.

It all begins with the Constitution of the United States. This document broadly outlines the responsibilities of national and state governments. Each state then has its own constitution, which outlines the responsibilities of the local government.

The laws and regulations on the state level are made and enforced in each state's capital. The structure of the state government is set up much like the federal government—an executive branch, a legislative branch, and a judicial branch. A governor elected by popular vote runs each state.

The governor of a state has many jobs. Governors submit the state budgets each year and prioritize spending. They have military powers and can declare disaster areas within their states. Governors meet with legislators to influence laws. They even have the authority to veto legislation. Governors can lessen a felon's sentence or spare a criminal's life.

In addition to a governor, a state has many other leaders. States have lieutenant governors who serve as second in command. They also have attorneys general, secretaries of state, legislators, and state treasurers.

Each state is divided into smaller subdivisions. Most states call these subdivisions *counties*. Counties must follow the rules of the state. States depend on county officials to protect residents' rights. The sheriff and the district attorney are two of the key players in county government. Through interviews, chapter 3 looks a little closer at the roles of these two offices.

The community government protects and serves the residents of towns or cities. Mayors are the heads of most cities. The mayor reports to the city council. Together they govern the city. Other city positions include the chief of police, the fire chief, and the director, or head, of the library. A superintendent, who is responsible for what happens in each school, runs the district's public schools.

From the president of the United States to the volunteers in U.S. communities, it is important for everyone to work together to keep the country strong and running smoothly.

Reading Exploration Essentials

Vocabulary

aldermen	assessment	at-large	bicameral
board	borough	capital punishment	charter
chief of police	city council	city manager	city manager-council
commission	concurrent	consolidate	contitutional convention
council	county	county assessor	county auditor
county clerk	county coroner	counter suveyor	delegate
district attorney	exclusive	executive clemency rules	federalism
figurehead	fire chief	general assembly	gubernatorial
house of delegates	house of representatives	legislator	mayor
ordinances	parish	president of the senate	prosecutor
ratify	representative	school district	senate
senator	sheriff	speaker	special education
statehouse	suffrage	superintendent	term
unicameral	veto	ward	zone

Reading Exploration

prereading

Draw a bull's-eye target on the board. Label each ring, starting in the center, with the levels of government—local community, city, county, state, and federal. Briefly discuss what the students know about each level of government.

during reading

As the students read *State and Local Government*, have then keep separate lists—one for each of the different levels of government. Ask them to add different job titles under each heading. For example, *sheriff* would go under the heading *County Government*.

postreading

Assign each student a job title listed under state, county, city, and local government. Challenge each student to find the name of the person currently holding that job. Add the names to your lists.

People in Politics

Government officials make and enforce the laws in Washington, D.C., as well as in your own state. Read through the following political positions. Show that you know the job of each political figure by using the job title in a complete sentence.

1. aldermen

_____

_____

2. chief of police

_____

_____

3. city manager

_____

_____

4. county assessor

_____

_____

5. county coroner

_____

_____

6. district attorney

_____

_____

continued

People in Politics *continued*

7. mayor

_____

_____

8. prosecutor

_____

_____

9. sheriff

_____

_____

10. superintendent

_____

_____

◎ **One Step Further:** Answer the following questions.

Who is the chief of police in your town?

_____

Who is the mayor of your town?

_____

Who is your school's superintendent?

_____

Levels of the U.S. Government

The United States has five levels of government—federal, state, county, city, and local community. Read through the list of words. Place each job title under the governmental heading with which it is best associated. The first one is done for you. You will not fill all of the blanks.

aldermen	chief of police	city council
commission	council	county auditor
district attorney	fire chief	governor
lieutenant governor	mayor	neighborhood association president
sheriff	state legislator	state treasurer
superintendent	teacher	U.S. legislators
U.S. president	U.S. Supreme Court	U.S. vice president

Federal Government

U.S. president
_____
_____
_____
_____

State Government

_____
_____
_____
_____
_____

County Government

_____
_____
_____
_____
_____

City Government

_____
_____
_____
_____
_____

Local Community Government

_____
_____
_____
_____
_____

continued

Levels of the U.S. Government *continued*

◎ **One Step Further:** Read about governors in *State and Local Government*. Find five words that would fit under each heading.

Jobs of the Governor

_____

_____

_____

_____

_____

Past Governors

_____

_____

_____

_____

_____

A Classified Government

Read through each group of words below. One word or group of words does not belong with the others. Draw a line through the word or group of words that does not belong. Then decide what the other words have in common. Write your answer in the space provided. You may need to read back through the indicated chapters in *State and Local Government* to find the answers.

Example: federal   state   ~~board~~   city

They are all   <u>levels of U.S. government</u>   .

Chapter 1

1. making treaties   declaring war   establishing post offices   ratifying amendments

They are all   _____.

2. printing money   holding elections   issuing licenses   regulating trade within a state

They are all   _____.

3. borrowing money   collecting taxes   conducting foreign policy   building roads

They are all   _____.

Chapter 2

4. federal   executive   legislative   judicial

They are all   _____.

5. preparing ballots   reporting election results   interpreting state law   certifying elections

They are all   _____.

continued

| A Classified Government *continued* | | |

Chapter 3

6. counties   employees   parishes   boroughs

    They are all _____.

7. enforcing laws   storing birth   holding county   issuing business
                       certificates   prisoners   licenses

    They are all _____.

8. reading   math   foreign language   social studies

    They are all _____.

Chapter 4

9. cities   residents   towns   villages

    They are all _____.

10. sheriff   dog warden   plant manager   city historian

    They are all _____.

Dig a Little Deeper

In *State and Local Government* you read about many jobs that make up the different levels of U.S. government. Here's your chance to dig a little deeper into one of those jobs. Think about the jobs you learned about at the city or county levels. Find out more about the actual person who occupies that job in your local community by conducting an interview. Think about the interviews you read in chapter 3. Use the guidelines below to take you through the process.

1. Choose a person to interview. Here are some ideas:

sheriff	county auditor	county assessor	county surveyor
county clerk	district attorney	mayor	aldermen
city manager	chief of police	fire chief	library director

2. Set up an appointment with the person you have chosen. Use the telephone book to find the number of the chosen office.

3. Write out a list of questions, leaving plenty of space for note-taking under each question. Think about the following as you plan your questions.

    • What qualifications are needed for the job?

    • What are the duties?

    • What is the best part of the job?

    • What is challenging about the job?

    • What made the person choose this particular job?

4. Be on time for your scheduled meeting.

5. After the interview, be sure to thank the person for taking the time to answer your questions.

6. At home or at school, review the questions and answers. Write a brief paragraph summarizing the interview on a separate sheet of paper.

School Government

The three branches of government are the executive branch, the judicial branch, and the legislative branch. Think of your school as a community. How are the three branches of government represented in the school setting? Work with a partner to answer the questions below.

1. Who or what do you think acts as the legislative branch for your school? Explain your answer.

_____

_____

_____

_____

2. Who or what do you think acts as the executive branch for your school? Explain your answer.

_____

_____

_____

_____

3. Who or what do you think acts as the judicial branch for your school? Explain your answer.

_____

_____

_____

_____

4. What do you think about the three-branch government that you've described for your school? Could some changes be made to help your school run more smoothly? Explain your answer.

_____

_____

_____

_____

Project Ideas

Choose from the following project suggestions to show what you have learned about state and local government. You may want to work with a partner or in a small group. Share your finished project with your classmates.

◎ On a large sheet of posterboard, draw a Venn diagram comparing and contrasting the powers of national and state governments.

◎ Draw a large map labeling the counties, parishes, or boroughs within your state.

◎ Find out about your state's capital. Research the city or town and write a summary of your findings.

◎ Find out more about one of the governors, past or present, of your state. Organize the information you have gathered on a large poster.

◎ Look into school funding. How much money does the federal government provide for each student in your state? How much money does your state spend on average for its students? How do you feel about what you discovered? Write a letter to your state legislator expressing your feelings or concerns.

◎ Write a persuasive paragraph in favor of the D.A.R.E program at your school.

◎ Invite the superintendent to be a guest speaker in your classroom. Ask him or her to explain the job duties of a superintendent. Allow time for a question-and-answer period. Prior to the superintendent's arrival, have each of your classmates write out a question they'd like to ask. As time allows, have the superintendent answer the questions.

◎ Read a current issue of your local newspaper. Write a reflection paragraph about one of the politically minded articles you have read.

◎ Make your neighborhood a better place to live. Organize a garbage pick-up with people in your neighborhood. Take photographs and put together a scrapbook to keep in your classroom.

◎ Research your state capitol building. How old is the building? What is housed there? Prepare a tabletop display to share what you've learned.

Twenty-Question Objective Test

Directions: Match each word and its meaning.

_____ 1. aldermen   a. elected official who heads a city government

_____ 2. county   b. of or relating to a governor

_____ 3. gubernatorial   c. members of a city council

_____ 4. mayor   d. head of a school district

_____ 5. superintendent   e. political subdivision of a state

Directions: Answer each statement True (T) or False (F).

_____ 6. A multilevel government gives a few people power.

_____ 7. The 19th Amendment to the Constitution made slavery illegal.

_____ 8. A governor is the head of a state's government.

_____ 9. All counties collect taxes.

_____ 10. Most United States residents are guaranteed a free public education.

Directions: Choose the best answer to complete each statement.

11. Concurrent powers are powers
    a. held only by the federal government.
    b. held only by the state government.
    c. shared between the federal and state government.

12. The center of the government is
    a. county government.
    b. city government.
    c. local community.

continued

State and Local Government
Twenty-Question Objective Test continued

13. The building in which the legislators meet is called the
    a. capital.
    b. capitol.
    c. convention hall.

14. The head of a state's government is called a
    a. governor.
    b. sheriff.
    c. president.

15. The first state with a female governor was
    a. Texas.
    b. Virginia.
    c. Wyoming.

16. Louisiana doesn't have counties; instead they are called
    a. boroughs.
    b. parishes.
    c. townships.

17. A person who has not graduated from college can earn a high school equivalency diploma by taking the
    a. DST.
    b. GED.
    c. DTG.

18. Rules and regulations that the council thinks will make the city a better place to live are called
    a. charters.
    b. zones.
    c. ordinances.

19. Most money for public schools comes from
    a. private donations.
    b. tuition.
    c. local property taxes.

continued

State and Local Government

Twenty-Question Objective Test continued

Directions: Answer the question using complete sentences.

20. What is the job of a governor?

_____

_____

_____

_____

_____

_____

_____

Answer Key

Elections and Political Parties

It's a Match! (page 17)
1. f; 2. b; 3. i; 4. h; 5. c; 6. a; 7. g; 8. j; 9. e; 10. d
One Step Further: 11. amendment; 12. ballot; 13. candidate; 14. debate; 15. delegate; 16. dictator; 17. moderator; 18. nominate; 19. platform; 20. suffrage

Instant Recall (page 18)
1. Election Day is the first Tuesday after the first Monday in November. 2. The minimum voting age in the United States is 18. 3. *Democracy* means "government by the people." 4. A new governor is elected every four years. 5. The first caucus in the election process is held in Iowa. 6. The first primary in the election process is held in New Hampshire. 7. A candidate needs 270 electoral votes to win a presidential election. 8. Answers will vary according to states. 9. The unofficial Democratic mascot is the donkey. 10. GOP stands for "Grand Old Party."

An Opinion Poll (page 19)
Answers may vary.

Dear Mr. President (page 21)
Answers may vary.

America Votes (page 22)

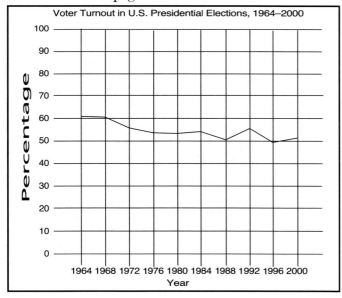

Twenty-Question Objective Test (page 24)

1. a; 2. c; 3. d; 4. e; 5. b; 6. F; 7. T; 8. F; 9. T; 10. F; 11. a; 12. a; 13. c; 14. b; 15. b; 16. c; 17. a; 18. c; 19. a; 20. Answers will vary, but may include the following: To contribute in my community I can help out by picking up trash or helping someone in need. I can read books and articles about important political issues. I can write letters to politicians voicing my concerns. I can help support a political candidate by helping to pass out flyers or hang posters. I can also participate in or organize fund-raisers for special causes.

The Executive Branch

Executive Branch Crossword (page 29)

Across: 1. amend; 2. jurisdiction; 3. policy; 4. precedent; 5. succeed; 6. veteran

Down: 7. perjury; 8. impeachment; 9. confirmed; 10. domestic; 11. resign; 12. discontent

Ordering the Facts (page 31)

Group 1: 1; 5; 2; 3; 4

Group 2: 4; 3; 1; 5; 2

Group 3: 2; 4; 3; 1; 5

Sticking with the Main Idea (page 32)

1. a; omit The vice president's office is in the West Wing of the White House. 2. c; omit Camp David is a popular vacation spot for the president. 3. b; omit The Department of Interior oversees memorial sites in Washington, D.C. 4. c; omit The Department of State is the oldest cabinet department. 5. a; omit President George W. Bush created the Office of Faith-Based and Community Initiatives in 2001.

A Presidential Biography (page 34)

Answers may vary.

Reading a Timeline (page 35)

1. 1888; 2. 1798; 3. the 22nd Amendment; 4. 14 years; 5. the Office of Homeland Security; 6. 1947; 7. 4 years

Twenty-Question Objective Test (page 38)

1. b; 2. e; 3. d; 4. c; 5. a; 6. T; 7. T; 8. F; 9. F; 10. T; 11. c; 12. c; 13. a; 14. b; 15. c; 16. b; 17. a; 18. b; 19. c; 20. Answers will vary, but may include the following: The president has both formal and informal powers. According to the Constitution, the president is the commander in chief of the armed forces. He appoints the head of each executive department. He grants pardons for crimes other than impeachment. The president makes treaties with the advice and consent of Congress. He nominates and appoints various positions. He presents a State of the Union address to Congress. He is host to representatives of foreign countries. The president makes legislative recommendations to Congress. He also makes sure that all laws are faithfully executed.

The Judicial Branch

The Word in Government (page 43)

1. petition; 2. defendant; 3. appeal; 4. justice; 5. seniority; 6. docket; 7. federal; 8. plaintiff;
9. opinion; 10. litigants
One Step Further: 11. appeal; 12. defendant; 13. docket; 14. federal; 15. justice; 16. litigants;
17. opinions; 18. petition; 19. plaintiff; 20. seniority

Expressing Yourself (page 44)

Answers may vary.

An Eye for an Eye (page 46)

1. b; 2. d; 3. e; 4. c; 5. a; 6. h; 7. j; 8. f; 9. i; 10. g

Supreme Court Justices (page 47)

Answers may vary.

Supreme Court Building (page 49)

Model construction will vary.

Twenty-Question Objective Test (page 51)

1. e; 2. a; 3. b; 4. d; 5. c; 6. F; 7. F; 8. T; 9. T; 10. F; 11. a; 12. c; 13. a; 14. b; 15. c; 16. b;
17. b; 18. a; 19. c; 20. Answers may vary.

The Legislative Branch

Hearing Double (page 56)

1. chamber; 2. bill; 3. chamber; 4. whip; 5. capital; 6. hearing; 7. hearing; 8. bill; 9. floor;
10. bill; 11. floor; 12. capital; 13. whip

House vs. Senate (page 58)

Answers may vary. Refer to the chart on page 8 of *The Legislative Branch*.

Congress Declares War (page 59)

Answers may vary.

Conquering the Nation's Debt (page 61)

Answers may vary.

A "Capital" Vacation Spot (page 62)
Answers may vary.

Twenty-Question Objective Test (page 64)
1. d; 2. a; 3. e; 4. b; 5. c; 6. T; 7. T; 8. T; 9. F; 10. F; 11. a; 12. b; 13. c; 14. a; 15. c; 16. b; 17. b; 18. a; 19. a; 20. Answers will vary, but may include the following: Similarities—Both senators and representatives represent their home states. Both groups meet in Washington, D.C. Members of both groups make laws. They are also both part of Congress. Differences—There are 435 representatives and only 100 senators. Senators are elected to six-year terms, whereas representatives are elected every two years. Senators must be at least 30 years old, but representatives only have to be at least 25 years old.

State and Local Government

People in Politics (page 69)
Answers may vary.

Levels of the U.S. Government (page 71)
   Federal Government
   U.S. president; U.S. legislators; U.S. Supreme Court; U.S. vice president

   State Government
   governor; lieutenant governor; state legislator; state treasurer

   County Government
   commission; sheriff; council; county auditor; district attorney

   City Government
   mayor; city council; aldermen; chief of police; fire chief

   Local Community Government
   neighborhood association president; superintendent; teacher

A Classified Government (page 73)
1. ratifying amendments/powers exclusive to the federal government; 2. printing money/powers exclusive to individual state governments; 3. conducting foreign policy/powers shared between the federal and state governments; 4. federal/branches of the U.S. government; 5. interpreting state law/jobs of the Secretary of State; 6. employees/subdivisions of states; 7. issuing business licenses/jobs of county officials; 8. foreign language/tests that make up the GED; 9. residents/places where people live; 10. sheriff/city positions

Dig a Little Deeper (page 75)

Answers may vary.

School Government (page 76)

Answers may vary.

Twenty-Question Objective Test (page 78)

1. c; 2. e; 3. b; 4. a; 5. d; 6. F; 7. F; 8. T; 9. T; 10. F; 11. c; 12. c; 13. b; 14. a; 15. c; 16. b; 17. b; 18. c; 19. c; 20. Answers will vary, but may include the following: A governor leads the state's government. The governor submits the state budget to the state legislature each year. He or she has certain military powers. The governor can declare natural disaster areas within their states. A governor represents the people of his or her state. In most states, the governor has the authority to override legislation. A governor can even spare a criminal's life.